Paint and Pretend
TEA SET

This edition published in 2017
By SpiceBox™
12171 Horseshoe Way
Richmond, BC
Canada V7A 4V4

First published in 2009
English text, design and layout copyright © SpiceBox™ 2008

ISBN 10: 1-77132-267-5
ISBN 13: 978-1-77132-267-6

CEO & Publisher: Ben Lotfi
Editorial: Ania Jaraczewski
Creative Director: Garett Chan
Art Director: Christine Covert
Design & Layout: Charmaine Muzyka
Illustrations: Morgan Price
Production: James Badger, Mell D'Clute
Sourcing: Tony Su, May Ko

Photo Credits: Dreamstime, pages 4, 37, 39,41; iStockphoto, pages 17, 19, 25, 36, 46, 48, 49; Shutterstock, pages 16, 17, 21, 43, 45.

For more SpiceBox products and information, visit our website:
www.spiceboxbooks.com

Manufactured in China

3 5 7 9 10 8 6 4

TABLE OF CONTENTS

Here are the fun activi-teas in the book

THE TEA PARTY

An introduction

A tea party is the perfect occasion to dress up and invite your friends over for a wonderful afternoon of playing games, eating special food and drinking tea, or just gathering your dolls and teddies and having a pretend party with your very own tea set that you painted yourself.

Let's get ready...it's time to have a tea party!

PAINT AND PRETEND

Instructions for painting your tea set
(and not your mom's furniture)

This miniature tea set is perfect for a pretend tea party for your dolls or stuffed bears. But if you are serving food or tea to people, make sure you use regular plates and cups from your kitchen.

Your tea set includes:

Four cups and saucers
Four larger plates
A teapot
A sugar bowl
A creamer
Brushes and loads of special paints you can use to decorate your set.

INSTRUCTIONS

1. Ask an adult to help you cover your work surface with paper to catch spills. Next, take your tea set out of the box and carefully wipe each piece with a damp paper towel to remove any smudges.

2. Arrange your painting supplies. Carefully cut your strips of paint into smaller sections. This will make your paints less tippy once they are open. Put a cup of clean water nearby, and keep some paper towels handy to wipe up spills and dry your brushes.

3. Now you are ready to paint! There are lots of fun ideas for designs on the next few pages. You can take inspiration from them, or use your imagination to come up with your own pretty patterns.

4. If you make a mistake while you are painting, or you change your mind, you can wash the paint off of the piece you are working on with warm soapy water. If it has already dried, you may need to scrub a bit with a cloth, but it will come off. Then start again!

5. Once you are happy with your tea set, let it dry for at least 6 hours.

6. Ask an adult to turn the oven on and heat it up to 350°F (180°C).

7. Place your tea set on a baking tray and ask an adult to put the tray in the oven.

8. Set the timer for 25 minutes, and let your tea set bake. This will make the paint fix permanently to the tea set. You will be able to get it wet and the paint won't come off.

9. Once the timer buzzes, ask an adult to take your tea set out of the oven. Let it cool completely.

10. Use your tea set for pretend tea parties, but remember not to use it for real food or drinks!

HOW TO HAVE A TEA PARTY

A history of crust-free sandwiches

Tea parties have been popular for over 150 years. Originally the only people invited to tea parties were royalty and their friends. Everyone wore beautiful gowns, gloves and fancy hats. Tea and treats like tiny sandwiches and cookies were served on pretty china cups and plates.

Nowadays, most of us aren't real princesses, or have royal friends, but it is so much fun to dress up and pretend! The next few pages have lots of fun ideas to help you host your own party.

INVITATIONS AND DRESS-UP

What to wear for a tea time affair

On pages 51 to 56 you will find pre-printed invitations for a Royal Tea Party. Cut these out and fill in the time, date and place of your tea party and give them to your friends so they can plan to attend your party. On the invitations, you should also let your guests know that they should dress up in their best party costumes!

Here are some fun suggestions if you and your friends need help planning what to wear:

Pretty dresses, or a fancy cape
Fancy shoes and purses
Tiaras and crowns
Hats and bonnets
Lots of jewelry!
Scepters or fans
Fancy gloves

Invitation Ideas:

After you have used the invitations in this book, you will want to make your own invitations. Here are some great ideas for invitations.

Make cards and decorate them with:
Glitter glue
Scraps of gift wrap
Stickers
Ribbon
Craft gems
Sequins

Use stickers and add decorations to your invitations that match the theme of your party.

TEA FOR TWO

In this section you will find plenty of great ideas for hosting your tea party

SETTING YOUR TABLE

Make it pret-tea

Now it is time to set your table. Take some time to decorate the table with a lovely tablecloth, flowers and doilies. Use your hand-painted tea set as a decorative centerpiece. Ask an adult for some dishes from the kitchen and lay out a cup and saucer, a plate and a pretty napkin at each setting. For a special touch, write each guest's name on one of the place cards from the back of the book, and put one by each place setting so your guests know where to sit when they arrive.

FOOD IDEAS

Taste-tea treats to serve your friends

There are lots of great ideas for yummy food to serve at a tea party, but try to serve things that are easy to eat daintily with your fingers. You and your friends will have fun nibbling bite-size snacks, so think of things that are small and won't be too messy. Little candies, cookies and fruit are always good. On the next few pages are some recipes for other tea party favorites. Remember that your mini tea set is for decoration only at this party. Use regular plates for serving food.

JELLY FRUIT WEDGES

Ingredients:

Oranges
Orange gelatin mix

Tools:

Tinfoil
Cookie sheet
A knife

Prepare the jelly mix as directed on the box. Crumple some tinfoil into circles and put them in a pan. Slice the orange in half and scoop out the fruit so only the peel remains.

Fill the orange shells with the prepared jelly and place on the tinfoil circles so that they don't tip over. Place in the fridge to set. Slice the jelly oranges into wedges and serve!

You can make a lot of yummy treats with jelly. Here is another recipe that is fun and easy for everyone!

JELLY CUPCAKES

Flavored gelatin
Whipped cream
Candies or sprinkles

1. To make jelly cupcakes, prepare your favorite flavor of jelly according to the package directions.
2. Pour into foil liners in a cupcake pan. (Don't use paper liners!)
3. Refrigerate for 4 hours or more until firm.
4. Frost the cupcake with the whipped cream and add the candies or sprinkles for a pretty and tasty treat.

MINI S'MORES

Ingredients:

Graham wafer cereal
Mini marshmallows
Chocolate chips

Use graham wafer cereal, mini marshmallows and chocolate chips to build mini s'mores. Microwave them for 10 seconds until the marshmallows and chocolate have melted. What a yummy treat!

OREO CAKES

Make tiny cakes with mini Oreo cookies. Frost the cookies carefully and decorate with sugar flowers or sprinkles.

PINWHEEL SANDWICHES

Ingredients:

Sandwich bread
Your favorite jam
Peanut butter

Tools:

Rolling pin
A butter knife

Cut the crusts off of a piece of sandwich bread and gently flatten it with a rolling pin. Spread the bread with jam or peanut butter. Roll the bread up carefully and cut the roll into slices. Dust the pinwheel sandwiches with icing sugar.

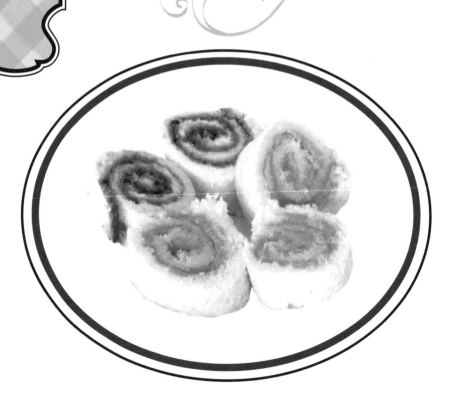

LAYERED SANDWICHES

Ingredients:

Cream cheese
Sandwich bread
Cucumber slices

Tools:

Cutting knife
A butter knife

Spread a piece of bread with cream cheese and put a second piece of bread on top. Spread the top of your sandwich with thin slices of cucumber and then top with another piece of bread. Cut the crusts off of your sandwich and then cut it in half. Cut each half into 3 small triangles.

TINY SUGAR COOKIES

Ingredients:

Sugar cookie dough
Icing sugar
Water
Food coloring
Sprinkles

Tools:

Cookie cutters
Rolling pin
Cookie sheet
A teaspoon

Purchase a roll of sugar cookie dough, and roll half of the dough out into a thin sheet about ¼ in (0.5 cm) thick. Use small cookie cutters to cut out your favorite shapes. Have an adult heat the oven according to the package instructions, and bake the cookies for 5 minutes. Because they are small, they won't need to bake for as long as the package directs.

If they don't look golden, bake for 1 or 2 minutes longer, checking to make sure they don't burn. To ice the cookies, mix half a cup of icing sugar and two tablespoons of warm water to make a runny glaze. Add a drop of food coloring if you wish. Using the tip of a spoon, drizzle the icing over the cookies and let it set.

JAM HEARTS

You will need one large and one small heart-shaped cookie cutter. Cut two large hearts out of a slice of bread. Spread your favorite jam on one of the hearts. Then gently flatten the second heart with your hand or a small rolling pin. Use the small cutter and cut a little heart out of the center of the large heart. Place the second slice on top of the heart that has jam on it.

FRUIT SKEWERS

Ingredients:

All of your favorite fruit

Tools:

Decorative skewers

Find or decorate toothpicks so that they match the theme of your party. Use them to spear small pieces of melon, strawberries and grapes. Yum!

WHAT TO DRINK

When you're thirst-tea!

At a traditional grown-up tea party, they likely will serve real tea. However, you and your friends might enjoy other drinks more. Here are some suggestions:

Lemonade
Fruit punch
Ice tea
Hot chocolate

GAMES TO PLAY

Classic party entertainment ideas

A tea party is a time to visit with your friends, eat the food that you made and sip your tea. However, you may want to have a special game prepared to play as well. This will encourage your friends to laugh and have a good time at your party. If it is a nice day, play outside and enjoy pretending that you are royalty attending a party, fairies attending a magical celebration, or adventurers on a jungle safari. However, if it is a drizzly day and you need to play inside, here are some classic games that are lots of fun.

MUSICAL THRONES

Line up chairs for everyone at your party. Decorate one chair so that it looks like a throne by draping it with a blanket and tinsel or other decorations you have made. Have everyone sit in a chair, then ask an adult to play some music. As the music is playing, everyone must walk around all of the chairs while the adult moves one chair away. After everyone has marched around the chairs in a procession for a minute or so, the adult should stop the music and everyone must try to sit in one of the remaining chairs. Because there is one less chair, one person will not be able to sit down without sitting on top of someone else! That person is now out of the game. Start the music again and take away another chair. Keep going until the only chair left is the throne, and only one person is able to sit down in it. Award the winner a paper crown to wear for the rest of the day!

I SPY

This is a very old, traditional game that was played by royalty at tea parties long ago. Start the game by picking an object in the room without telling anyone what it is. Say, "I spy with my little eye, something that is _____," and tell them what color it is. Have everyone guess what the object is until your guests figure it out. Another way to play this game is to have everyone cover their eyes while you remove an item from the room. Then have your guests try to guess which object is missing.

TREASURE HUNTS

These require a bit of planning and probably you will need some help from an adult, but they are so much fun that everyone will love playing! To create a treasure hunt, you will need to write a bunch of clues such as:

"When my teddy goes to bed at night, this is where he sleeps." (Place the next clue near your pillow.)

"A queen sits on this." (Tape a clue under the chair that you decorated as a throne.)

Continue to place clues around your home until you have finally found a spot to hide a small treasure. Perhaps it will be cookies, some chocolates or a small toy, but be sure to have something for everyone who plays! Don't forget to hand your guests the first clue to start them on their way.

Another way to set up a treasure hunt is to decide on a symbol that your guests can look for, like the picture of a crown, a flower or a butterfly. Tape them around your house and draw arrows from one to symbol to the next for your guests to follow until they find the treasure.

OTHER PARTY THEMES

Any time is a good time to par-tea!

After you host a royal tea party, you may want to plan a tea party with another theme! Themes are fun because they encourage your friends to dress up and play imaginative games. You can also create matching invitations as well as decorations and special games and foods. Here are some fun ideas:

Ballerina Tea Party: Wear your favorite tutus and ballet slippers, and with your friends plan and present a ballet performance for your parents.

Teddy Bear Picnic: If you want to have a party without inviting friends over, then why not invite your favorite teddy bears and dolls? They are wonderful company and will happily play all of your games and use your mini tea set! Be sure to read Winnie the Pooh to them.

Mommy & Me Party: Invite your mother to be your special guest at your next party. Why don't you and your mother put on your favorite dresses and create a pretty flower bouquet for your table? A fun activity to do together would be to look at photos of your mom when she was your age.

Magical Fairy Tea: Make fairy cakes and dance in a toadstool ring as you and your friends celebrate being fairies! Be sure to wear your fairy wings, and if you don't have any, they are loads of fun to make with craft paper and sparkles. You can also make fairy wands out of drinking straws, tinsel and ribbons.

Safari Party: Invite your friends to bring their favorite stuffed jungle animal and plan a safari around your backyard or in a park. Plan a scavenger hunt and look for special leaves, flowers, insects or rocks to win prizes. You could also paint jungle animals on rocks for a fun craft that your guests can then take home with them for their own yards.

INVITATIONS AND PLACE CARDS

Ready-to-go place cards and invitations

Carefully cut out the invitations and fold them in half. Fill them out, decorate them and give them to your special guests. Press out the place cards and write your guests' names on them. Set them by their tea cup at the table so they know where to sit.

YOU'RE
INVITED
TO A
TEA PARTY!

YOU'RE
INVITED
TO A
TEA PARTY!

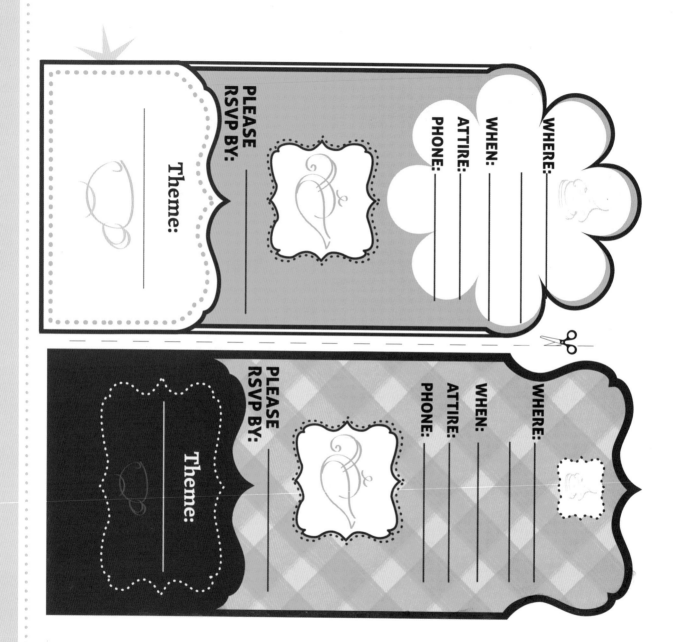

PLEASE
RSVP BY:

Theme:

WHERE:

WHEN:

ATTIRE:

PHONE:

PLEASE
RSVP BY:

Theme:

WHERE:

WHEN:

ATTIRE:

PHONE:

YOU'RE
INVITED
TO A
TEA PARTY!

YOU'RE
INVITED
TO A
TEA PARTY!

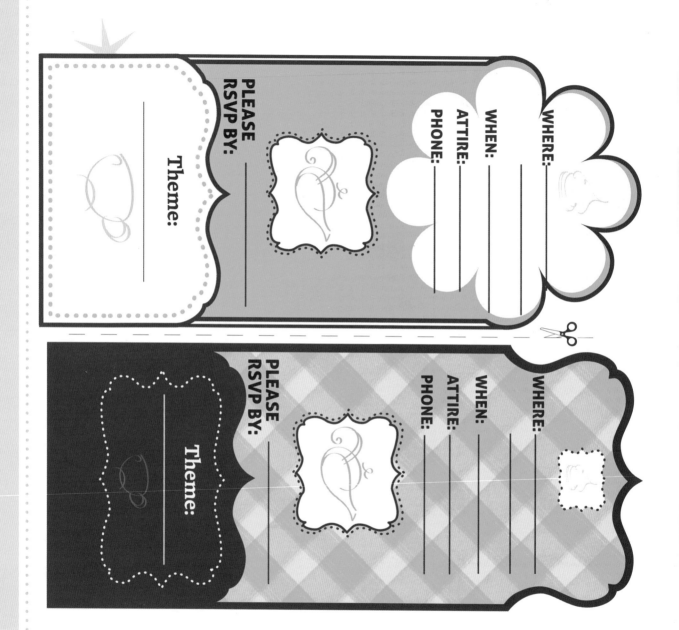

PLEASE
RSVP BY:

Theme:

WHERE:

WHEN:

ATTIRE:

PHONE:

PLEASE
RSVP BY:

Theme:

WHERE:

WHEN:

ATTIRE:

PHONE: